LET'S HEAR IT FOR DINNER, SNOOPY

**Also by the same author,
and available in Coronet Books:**

Let's Hear It For Dinner, Snoopy

Selected cartoons from Don't Hassle Me
With Your Sighs, Chuck Vol. 3

Charles M. Schulz

CORONET BOOKS
Hodder Fawcett London

Copyright © 1975, 1976 by United Feature
Syndicate, Inc.

First published in the United States by
Fawcett Publications, Inc.

Coronet edition 1980

British Library C.I.P.

Schulz, Charles Monroe
  Let's hear it for dinner, Snoopy.
  I. Title
  741.5'973   PN6728.P4

ISBN 0-340-25865-9

Reproduced, printed and bound in Great Britain for
Hodder Fawcett Ltd., Mill Road, Dunton Green,
Sevenoaks, Kent (Editorial Office: 47 Bedford
Square, London, WC1 3DP) by
Cox & Wyman Ltd., Reading

WHAT'S THIS I HEAR?
YOU CAN'T GO TO NEEDLES FOR THANKSGIVING...YOU'LL GET LOST IN THE DESERT!
YOU'LL BUMP INTO A CACTUS! IF YOU BUMP THAT BANANA NOSE OF YOURS INTO A CACTUS, YOU'LL BE IN REAL TROUBLE!
HOW GROSS!
SCHULZ

CHUCK! WHAT ARE YOU DOING IN MY SEAT?!
OUR SCHOOL BUILDING COLLAPSED SO WE HAVE TO COME HERE TO YOUR SCHOOL FOR AWHILE...
YOU MEAN WE'RE GONNA BE SHARING? WOW! THIS IS GREAT! SIDE BY SIDE, HUH?
LOOK OUT TODAY, MA'AM! YOU'RE GONNA BE DOUBLE-TEAMED!!